Mental Maths Tests

for ages 9–10

- ✓ **Ten complete Mental Maths timed tests, together with a pre-recorded CD**

- ✓ **Ideal practice for optional National Tests**

- ✓ **Bonus material includes record sheets, addition squares, and multiplication squares**

Introduction

Optional maths tests for Years 3, 4 and 5 can be given at any time during the school year depending on the individual teacher concerned. They allow teachers to monitor pupils' progress between the statutory tests at KS1 and KS2. The materials in this book provide practice for the type of questions that appear in the mental maths test but also for other aspects of mathematics at the appropriate levels indicated by the Numeracy framework.

By working through the tests with the pupils, teachers can gain valuable insights into their pupils' levels of performance. At the same time the children are gaining experience of working in a test situation, listening to recorded questions that are timed in the same way as the 'real' test.

General instructions for the administration of the tests

To make these tests seem as realistic as possible children should have clear desks and only a pen or pencil to write with. They should not be supplied with paper for working out the answers.

Before starting each test the children should write their name and school in the spaces provided.

Inform the children that:

- they should work individually and should not talk at all during the test;

- there will be 20 questions altogether;

- they will be allowed 5 seconds to answer each of the first five questions, 10 seconds for each of the next 10 questions, and 15 seconds for each of the last five questions;

- for some questions, some information will be provided on the test sheet;

- calculators or other equipment are not allowed;

- they should not rub out answers but, if they wish to change them, they can cross them out and write their new answers next to the incorrect ones;

- if they cannot do a question they should put a cross in the answer box.

Andrew Brodie: Mental Maths Tests 9–10 © A & C Black

Test 1

Before playing the test on the CD give each child a copy of the test and read out the following script:

Listen to the instructions carefully. I will answer any questions that you have after I have finished reading the instructions to you. Once the test starts you will not be able to ask any questions.

The first question is a practice question. In the test there will then be twenty questions.

Each question has an answer box. Make sure that you only write the answer to the correct question in the box. Try to work out each answer in your head. You can make notes outside the answer box if this helps you but do not try to write out calculations because you will not have enough time. For some questions you will find important information already provided for you.

Each question will be read out twice. Listen carefully then work out your answer. If you cannot do the question, just put a cross. If you make a mistake, do not rub out the wrong answer; cross it out and write the correct answer.

Some questions are easy and some are more difficult. Do not worry if you find a question hard; just do your best. I hope that you enjoy the test.

At this point, answer any questions that the children ask.

Now listen carefully to the practice question. You will hear the question twice, then you will have five seconds to work out and write down the answer.

   What is three add four?

   What is three add four?

Allow the children five seconds to write the answer, then say:

Put your pencil down.

Check that the children have written the answer to the practice question in the practice question answer box. Remind them that they cannot ask any more questions once the test is started. When you are ready, press start on your CD player.

When the test is finished ask the children to stop writing, then collect the test sheets. For ease of marking we have created a copy of the test paper with the answers entered in the appropriate boxes.

Questions for Test 1

For each of the first five questions you have five seconds to work out and write down the answer.

1   What must be added to thirty-eight to make fifty?

2   What number is half of forty-two?

3   Look at your answer sheet. Draw a ring around the number thirty thousand.

4   Multiply five point six by ten.

5   What is thirty-one take away nine?

For each of the next questions you have ten seconds to work out and write down the answer.

6   Write the biggest integer you can using the digits three, seven, six, zero, four.

7   What is two hundred multiplied by one hundred?

8   I have a five pound note. I buy a magazine for two pounds forty pence. How much change do I receive?

9   What is five times three times two?

10   Jasdeep is running around a four hundred metre track. She stops for a rest after two hundred and fifty metres. How much further has she got to run?

11   What number is ninety-nine more than two hundred and fifty-seven?

12   Write one quarter of a metre in millimetres.

13   How many days are there altogether in five weeks?

14   One thousand subtract six hundred and fifty.

15   A regular pentagon has sides of six centimetres. What is its perimeter?

For each of the next five questions you have fifteen seconds to work out and write down the answer.

16   How much money is one quarter of five pounds?

17   Four children share some stamps. They have two stamps each and there are three spare stamps. How many stamps are there altogether?

18   Add two thousand two hundred and fifty to four thousand five hundred and six.

19   How many five pound notes are there in two hundred and five pounds?

20   Look at your answer sheet. What number should be written in the box?

Put your pencil down. The test is over.

   Andrew Brodie: Mental Maths Tests 9–10 © A & C Black

Test 1

First name .... Last name ....

School ....

.... **Total marks**

Practice question

Five-second questions

1 | 38

2 | 42

3 | 300   3000   30 000   300 000

4

5

Ten-second questions

6 | 3, 7, 6, 0, 4

7

8 £ | £2.40

9 | 5 3 2

10 | m

11 | 257

12 | mm | $\frac{1}{4}$ m

13 | days

14

15 | cm

Fifteen-second questions

16 £

17 | stamps

18 | 4506

19 | £205

20 | $36 + \boxed{} = 42 + 8$

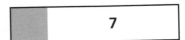

Test 1 Answers

Practice question

	7

Five-second questions

1	**12**	38

2	**21**	42

3		
300	3000	(30 000)	300 000

4	**56**

5	**22**

Ten-second questions

6	**76 430**	3, 7, 6, 0, 4

7	**20 000**

8	**£2.60**	£2.40

9	**30**	5 3 2

10	**150** m

11	**356**	257

12	**250** mm	$\frac{1}{4}$ m

13	**35** days

14	**350**

15	**30** cm

Fifteen-second questions

16	**£1.25**

17	**11** stamps

18	**6756**	4506

19	**41**	£205

20	
	36 + **14** = 42 + 8

Test 2

Before playing the test on the CD give each child a copy of the test and read out the following script:

> **Listen to the instructions carefully. I will answer any questions that you have after I have finished reading the instructions to you. Once the test starts you will not be able to ask any questions.**
>
> **The first question is a practice question. In the test there will then be twenty questions.**
>
> **Each question has an answer box. Make sure that you only write the answer to the correct question in the box. Try to work out each answer in your head. You can make notes outside the answer box if this helps you but do not try to write out calculations because you will not have enough time. For some questions you will find important information already provided for you.**
>
> **Each question will be read out twice. Listen carefully then work out your answer. If you cannot do the question, just put a cross. If you make a mistake, do not rub out the wrong answer; cross it out and write the correct answer.**
>
> **Some questions are easy and some are more difficult. Do not worry if you find a question hard; just do your best. I hope that you enjoy the test.**

At this point, answer any questions that the children ask.

> **Now listen carefully to the practice question. You will hear the question twice, then you will have five seconds to work out and write down the answer.**
>
> *What is six minus two?*
>
> *What is six minus two?*

Allow the children five seconds to write the answer, then say:

Put your pencil down.

Check that the children have written the answer to the practice question in the practice question answer box. Remind them that they cannot ask any more questions once the test is started. When you are ready, press start on your CD player.

When the test is finished ask the children to stop writing, then collect the test sheets. For ease of marking we have created a copy of the test paper with the answers entered in the appropriate boxes.

Questions for Test 2

For each of the first five questions you have five seconds to work out and write down the answer.

1   What is the product of three and six?

2   Write one tenth as a decimal.

3   Forty-three subtract eleven.

4   What is seven hundred times ten?

5   Share thirty-two between eight.

For each of the next questions you have ten seconds to work out and write down the answer.

6   Amy pours three hundred grams out of a one kilogram bag of sugar. How much sugar is left in the bag?

7   What is one point seven add one point four?

8   Look at your answer sheet. What temperature does the thermometer show?

9   Write six point five metres in centimetres.

10   A plane journey takes thirteen hours. What fraction of a whole day is this?

11   Forty-five percent of the children in a class have school meals. What percentage do not have school meals?

12   A rectangle is six centimetres long and four centimetres wide. What is its area?

13   One thousand five hundred and forty-nine subtract seven hundred.

14   What is double one hundred and forty?

15   Increase three hundred and eighty by forty-two.

For each of the next five questions you have fifteen seconds to work out and write down the answer.

16   How much money is three quarters of ten pounds?

17   Look at your answer sheet. What number should be written in the box?

18   I buy a magazine for two pounds fifty-five pence and a notebook for one pound fifteen pence. How much do I spend altogether?

19   A television programme starts at six fifty-five and finishes at seven twenty-six. How many minutes long is the programme?

20   What is twenty-five percent of five hundred pounds?

Put your pencil down. The test is over.

   Andrew Brodie: Mental Maths Tests 9–10 © A & C Black

Test 2

First name .... Last name ....

School ....

.... **Total marks**

Practice question

[ ]

Five-second questions

1	

2	

3	

4	700

5	

Ten-second questions

6	g	300 g

7	1.7 1.4

8	°C

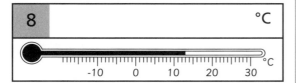

9	cm	6.5 m

10	13 hours

11	%	45%

12	cm²

13	1549

14	

15	380

Fifteen-second questions

16	£	$\frac{3}{4}$

17	6 + 14 = 3 + [ ]

18	£	£2.55 £1.15

19	minutes	6.55 pm

20	£	

Test 2 Answers

Practice question

	4

Five-second questions

1	18

2	0.1

3	32

4	7000	700

5	4

Ten-second questions

6	700 g	300 g

7	3.1	1.7 1.4

8	13 °C

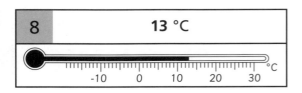

9	650 cm	6.5 m

10	$\frac{13}{24}$	13 hours

11	55%	45%

12	24 cm²

13	849	1549

14	280

15	422	380

Fifteen-second questions

16	£7.50	$\frac{3}{4}$

17	

$$6 + 14 = 3 + \boxed{17}$$

18	£3.70	£2.55 £1.15

19	31 minutes	6.55 pm

20	£125

Andrew Brodie: Mental Maths Tests 9–10 © A & C Black

Test 3

Before playing the test on the CD give each child a copy of the test and read out the following script:

> **Listen to the instructions carefully. I will answer any questions that you have after I have finished reading the instructions to you. Once the test starts you will not be able to ask any questions.**
>
> **The first question is a practice question. In the test there will then be twenty questions.**
>
> **Each question has an answer box. Make sure that you only write the answer to the correct question in the box. Try to work out each answer in your head. You can make notes outside the answer box if this helps you but do not try to write out calculations because you will not have enough time. For some questions you will find important information already provided for you.**
>
> **Each question will be read out twice. Listen carefully then work out your answer. If you cannot do the question, just put a cross. If you make a mistake, do not rub out the wrong answer; cross it out and write the correct answer.**
>
> **Some questions are easy and some are more difficult. Do not worry if you find a question hard; just do your best. I hope that you enjoy the test.**

At this point, answer any questions that the children ask.

> **Now listen carefully to the practice question. You will hear the question twice, then you will have five seconds to work out and write down the answer.**
>
> *What is nine add two?*
>
> *What is nine add two?*

Allow the children five seconds to write the answer, then say:

Put your pencil down.

Check that the children have written the answer to the practice question in the practice question answer box. Remind them that they cannot ask any more questions once the test is started. When you are ready, press start on your CD player.

When the test is finished ask the children to stop writing, then collect the test sheets. For ease of marking we have created a copy of the test paper with the answers entered in the appropriate boxes.

Questions for Test 3

For each of the first five questions you have five seconds to work out and write down the answer.

1. What is nine hundred divided by ten?

2. What is three squared?

3. What must be added to seventy-two to make one hundred?

4. Zero point four times ten.

5. How many hundreds make three thousand six hundred?

For each of the next questions you have ten seconds to work out and write down the answer.

6. Write the smallest integer you can using the digits six, nine, seven, four and three.

7. What number is ninety-nine more than five hundred and twenty-three?

8. What percentage is equivalent to one half?

9. A regular hexagon has sides of five centimetres. What is its perimeter?

10. Write one quarter of a litre in millilitres.

11. What number is halfway between three thousand six hundred and four thousand?

12. Write the next number in this sequence: thirteen, sixteen, nineteen, twenty-two.

13. Look at your answer sheet. How much water is in the measuring cylinder?

14. Decrease four hundred and ten by thirty-five.

15. What is half of two hundred and fifty?

For each of the next five questions you have fifteen seconds to work out and write down the answer.

16. What is the total of twenty-four, sixteen and thirty-two?

17. How many edges does a cuboid have?

18. Look at your answer sheet. What number should be written in the box?

19. Look at your answer sheet. Draw a ring around the number that is divisible by seven.

20. Add four hundred to three thousand seven hundred and twenty-five.

Put your pencil down. The test is over.

Test 3

First name .... Last name ....

School ....

....

Total marks

Practice question

Five-second questions

1	

2	

3	72

4	0.4

5	3600

Ten-second questions

6	6, 9, 7, 4, 3

7	523

8	%	$\frac{1}{2}$

9	cm

10	ml	$\frac{1}{4}$ l

11	3600

12	13, 16, 19, 22, , ...

13	ml	 400 ml 300 200 100

14	410

15	

Fifteen-second questions

16	24, 16, 32

17	

18	40 – ☐ = 4 x 8

19	46 47 48 49 50

20	3725

Test 3 Answers

Practice question

	11

Five-second questions

1	90

2	9

3	28	72

4	4	0.4

5	36	3600

Ten-second questions

6	34 679	6, 9, 7, 4, 3

7	622	523

8	50 %	$\frac{1}{2}$

9	30 cm

10	250 ml	$\frac{1}{4}$ l

11	3800	3600

12	13, 16, 19, 22, 25

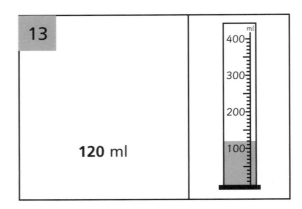

13	120 ml

14	375	410

15	125

Fifteen-second questions

16	72	24, 16, 32

17	12

18	40 − [8] = 4 x 8

19	46 47 48 (49) 50

20	4125	3725

Andrew Brodie: Mental Maths Tests 9–10 © A & C Black

Test 4

Before playing the test on the CD give each child a copy of the test and read out the following script:

Listen to the instructions carefully. I will answer any questions that you have after I have finished reading the instructions to you. Once the test starts you will not be able to ask any questions.

The first question is a practice question. In the test there will then be twenty questions.

Each question has an answer box. Make sure that you only write the answer to the correct question in the box. Try to work out each answer in your head. You can make notes outside the answer box if this helps you but do not try to write out calculations because you will not have enough time. For some questions you will find important information already provided for you.

Each question will be read out twice. Listen carefully then work out your answer. If you cannot do the question, just put a cross. If you make a mistake, do not rub out the wrong answer; cross it out and write the correct answer.

Some questions are easy and some are more difficult. Do not worry if you find a question hard; just do your best. I hope that you enjoy the test.

At this point, answer any questions that the children ask.

Now listen carefully to the practice question. You will hear the question twice, then you will have five seconds to work out and write down the answer.

> *What is eight take away four?*

> *What is eight take away four?*

Allow the children five seconds to write the answer, then say:

Put your pencil down.

Check that the children have written the answer to the practice question in the practice question answer box. Remind them that they cannot ask any more questions once the test is started. When you are ready, press start on your CD player.

When the test is finished ask the children to stop writing, then collect the test sheets. For ease of marking we have created a copy of the test paper with the answers entered in the appropriate boxes.

Questions for Test 4

For each of the first five questions you have five seconds to work out and write down the answer.

  1   What is the product of two and seven?

  2   What is half of six hundred and forty?

  3   Multiply twelve point nine by ten.

  4   What is the difference between twenty-seven and one hundred?

  5   Share twenty-four between three.

For each of the next questions you have ten seconds to work out and write down the answer.

  6   Look at your answer sheet. Draw a ring around the largest number.

  7   How many days are there altogether in seven weeks?

  8   What percentage is equivalent to one quarter?

  9   Round two thousand seven hundred and forty-seven to the nearest ten.

  10   Write the next number in this sequence: twenty-nine, thirty-three, thirty-seven, forty-one.

  11   What is ten percent of thirty pounds?

  12   Write four thousand five hundred grams in kilograms.

  13   Three hundred and forty add two hundred and fifty-seven.

  14   Tariq pours six hundred millilitres of water out of a one litre bottle. How much water is left in the bottle?

  15   What number is ninety-nine less than one thousand and one?

For each of the next five questions you have fifteen seconds to work out and write down the answer.

  16   Look at your answer sheet. Draw a ring around the number that is not a multiple of three.

  17   How much more is three thousand and five than nine hundred and ninety-five?

  18   I think of a number. I subtract three then divide by two. The answer is twelve. What was the number I first thought of?

  19   Look at your answer sheet. What is the size of the angle marked A?

  20   How many vertices does a tetrahedron have?

Put your pencil down. The test is over.

Andrew Brodie: Mental Maths Tests 9–10 © A & C Black

Test 4

First name .... Last name ....

School ....

.... **Total marks**

Practice question

Five-second questions

| 1 | |

| 2 | |

| 3 | 12.9 |

| 4 | 27 |

| 5 | |

Ten-second questions

| 6 | |

34 162   6213   41 236   4632

| 7 | days |

| 8 | % | $\frac{1}{4}$ |

| 9 | 2747 |

| 10 | 29, 33, 37, 41,   , ... |

| 11 | £ |

| 12 | kg | 4500 g |

| 13 | 257 |

| 14 | ml | 600 ml |

| 15 | 1001 |

Fifteen-second questions

| 16 | 12   16   18   21   27 |

| 17 | 3005 |

| 18 | 12 |

| 19 | ° |

A

60°

| 20 | |

Test 4 Answers

Practice question

	4

Five-second questions

1	14

2	320

3	129	12.9

4	73	27

5	8

Ten-second questions

6	
34 126 6213 (41 236) 4632	

7	49 days

8	25%	$\frac{1}{4}$

9	2750	2747

10	29, 33, 37, 41, 45

11	£3

12	4.5 kg	4500 g

13	597	257

14	400 ml	600 ml

15	902	1001

Fifteen-second questions

16	12 (16) 18 21 27

17	2010	3005

18	27	12

19	30 °

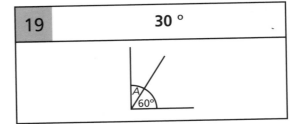

20	4

Test 5

Before playing the test on the CD give each child a copy of the test and read out the following script:

> **Listen to the instructions carefully. I will answer any questions that you have after I have finished reading the instructions to you. Once the test starts you will not be able to ask any questions.**
>
> **The first question is a practice question. In the test there will then be twenty questions.**
>
> **Each question has an answer box. Make sure that you only write the answer to the correct question in the box. Try to work out each answer in your head. You can make notes outside the answer box if this helps you but do not try to write out calculations because you will not have enough time. For some questions you will find important information already provided for you.**
>
> **Each question will be read out twice. Listen carefully then work out your answer. If you cannot do the question, just put a cross. If you make a mistake, do not rub out the wrong answer; cross it out and write the correct answer.**
>
> **Some questions are easy and some are more difficult. Do not worry if you find a question hard; just do your best. I hope that you enjoy the test.**

At this point, answer any questions that the children ask.

> **Now listen carefully to the practice question. You will hear the question twice, then you will have five seconds to work out and write down the answer.**
>
> *What is three add seven?*
>
> *What is three add seven?*

Allow the children five seconds to write the answer, then say:

> **Put your pencil down.**

Check that the children have written the answer to the practice question in the practice question answer box. Remind them that they cannot ask any more questions once the test is started. When you are ready, press start on your CD player.

When the test is finished ask the children to stop writing, then collect the test sheets. For ease of marking we have created a copy of the test paper with the answers entered in the appropriate boxes.

Questions for Test 5

For each of the first five questions you have five seconds to work out and write down the answer.

1   What is one tenth of eight hundred?

2   What is five squared?

3   Double forty-five.

4   What is the difference between thirty-five and one hundred?

5   Look at your answer sheet. Draw a ring around the larger number.

For each of the next questions you have ten seconds to work out and write down the answer.

6   I have a five pound note. I buy a box of tissues for one pound fifty pence. How much change do I receive?

7   What is four times two times five?

8   What number is ninety-nine more than three hundred and fifteen?

9   A regular octagon has sides of four centimetres. What is its perimeter?

10   Write one quarter of a kilometre in metres.

11   What number is half way between six thousand two hundred and seven thousand?

12   Round three thousand four hundred and ninety-three to the nearest hundred.

13   Look at your answer sheet. What temperature does the thermometer show?

14   A sea voyage takes seventeen hours. What fraction of a day is this?

15   Look at your answer sheet. Draw a ring around the time that is the same as six thirty pm.

For each of the next five questions you have fifteen seconds to work out and write down the answer.

16   What is the remainder when twenty-seven is divided by six?

17   How much money is one quarter of six pounds?

18   Look at your answer sheet. What number should be written in the box?

19   Add eight hundred to two thousand four hundred and sixty-eight.

20   I buy a book for six pounds ninety-nine pence and a map for seven pounds ninety-nine pence. How much do I spend altogether?

Put your pencil down. The test is over.

   Andrew Brodie: Mental Maths Tests 9–10 © A & C Black

Test 5

First name .... Last name ....

School ....

.... **Total marks**

Practice question

Five-second questions

1	

2	

3	45

4	35

5	14 793	14 973

Ten-second questions

6	£	£1.50

7		4 2 5

8		315

9	cm	

10		m	$\frac{1}{4}$ km

11		6200

12		3493

13		°C

14		17 hours

15	

16.30   17.30   18.30   19.30   20.30

Fifteen-second questions

16		27

17	£	£6

18	

$$60 - 4 = \boxed{} \times 8$$

19		2468

20	£	£6.99 £7.99

Test 5 Answers

Practice question

	10

Five-second questions

1	80

2	25

3	90	45

4	65	35

5	14 793	(**14 973**)

Ten-second questions

6	£3.50	£1.50

7	40	4 2 5

8	414	315

9	32 cm

10	250 m	$\frac{1}{4}$ km

11	6600	6200

12	3500	3493

13	27 °C

14	$\frac{17}{24}$	17 hours

15	

16.30   17.30   (18.30)   19.30   20.30

Fifteen-second questions

16	3	27

17	£1.50	£6

18	

60 − 4 = ☐7 x 8

19	3268	2468

20	£14.98	£6.99 £7.99

   Andrew Brodie: Mental Maths Tests 9–10 © A & C Black

Test 6

Before playing the test on the CD give each child a copy of the test and read out the following script:

Listen to the instructions carefully. I will answer any questions that you have after I have finished reading the instructions to you. Once the test starts you will not be able to ask any questions.

The first question is a practice question. In the test there will then be twenty questions.

Each question has an answer box. Make sure that you only write the answer to the correct question in the box. Try to work out each answer in your head. You can make notes outside the answer box if this helps you but do not try to write out calculations because you will not have enough time. For some questions you will find important information already provided for you.

Each question will be read out twice. Listen carefully then work out your answer. If you cannot do the question, just put a cross. If you make a mistake, do not rub out the wrong answer; cross it out and write the correct answer.

Some questions are easy and some are more difficult. Do not worry if you find a question hard; just do your best. I hope that you enjoy the test.

At this point, answer any questions that the children ask.

Now listen carefully to the practice question. You will hear the question twice, then you will have five seconds to work out and write down the answer.

What is half of six?

What is half of six?

Allow the children five seconds to write the answer, then say:

Put your pencil down.

Check that the children have written the answer to the practice question in the practice question answer box. Remind them that they cannot ask any more questions once the test is started. When you are ready, press start on your CD player.

When the test is finished ask the children to stop writing, then collect the test sheets. For ease of marking we have created a copy of the test paper with the answers entered in the appropriate boxes.

Questions for Test 6

For each of the first five questions you have five seconds to work out and write down the answer.

1   What is double six and a half?

2   What is the square of four?

3   Sixty-two subtract nine.

4   Write four tenths as a decimal.

5   Seventeen add thirteen.

For each of the next questions you have ten seconds to work out and write down the answer.

6   Write the biggest integer you can using the digits five, nine, eight, one and three.

7   Add two point nine to three point six.

8   How many days are there altogether in the last two months of the year?

9   What percentage is equivalent to three quarters?

10   Write three quarters of a metre in millimetres.

11   Round seven thousand three hundred and sixteen to the nearest ten.

12   Write the next number in this sequence: thirty-seven, forty-three, forty-nine, fifty-five.

13   What is ten percent of sixty pounds?

14   Sixty-five percent of a class of children do not have a pet at home. What percentage do have a pet?

15   Increase five hundred and seventy by sixty-seven.

For each of the next five questions you have fifteen seconds to work out and write down the answer.

16   Look at your answer sheet. Draw a ring around the number that is not a multiple of four.

17   Twenty-seven books are shared equally between four children. There are three books left over. How many books did each child receive?

18   How much less than five thousand and two is two thousand nine hundred and ninety-nine?

19   Look at your answer sheet. What number should be written in the box?

20   What is twenty-five percent of eight hundred pounds?

Put your pencil down. The test is over.

   Andrew Brodie: Mental Maths Tests 9–10 © A & C Black

Test 6

First name .... Last name ....

School ....

.... **Total marks** [ ]

Practice question

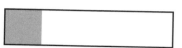

Five-second questions

| 1 | | $6\frac{1}{2}$ |

| 2 | |

| 3 | |

| 4 | |

| 5 | |

Ten-second questions

| 6 | | 5, 9, 8, 1, 3, |

| 7 | | 2.9   3.6 |

| 8 | days |

| 9 | % | $\frac{3}{4}$ |

| 10 | mm | $\frac{3}{4}$ m |

| 11 | | 7316 |

| 12 | 37,   43,   49,   55,   , ... |

| 13 | £ |

| 14 | % | 65% |

| 15 | | 570 |

Fifteen-second questions

| 16 | 8   16   24   30   36 |

| 17 | | 27 |

| 18 | | 5002 2999 |

| 19 | 50 ÷ 2 = 20 + [ ] |

| 20 | £ |

Practice question

	3

Five-second questions

1	**13**	$6\frac{1}{2}$

2	**16**

3	**53**

4	**0.4**

5	**30**

Ten-second questions

6	**98 531**	5, 9, 8, 1, 3,

7	**6.5**	2.9 3.6

8	**61** days

9	**75%**	$\frac{3}{4}$

10	**750** mm	$\frac{3}{4}$ m

11	**7320**	7316

12	37, 43, 49, 55, **61**, …

13	**£6**

14	**35%**	65%

15	**637**	570

Fifteen-second questions

16	8	16	24	(30)	36

17	**6**	27

18	**2003**	5002 2999

19	
	50 ÷ 2 = 20 + **5**

20	**£200**

Test 7

Before playing the test on the CD give each child a copy of the test and read out the following script:

> Listen to the instructions carefully. I will answer any questions that you have after I have finished reading the instructions to you. Once the test starts you will not be able to ask any questions.
>
> The first question is a practice question. In the test there will then be twenty questions.
>
> Each question has an answer box. Make sure that you only write the answer to the correct question in the box. Try to work out each answer in your head. You can make notes outside the answer box if this helps you but do not try to write out calculations because you will not have enough time. For some questions you will find important information already provided for you.
>
> Each question will be read out twice. Listen carefully then work out your answer. If you cannot do the question, just put a cross. If you make a mistake, do not rub out the wrong answer; cross it out and write the correct answer.
>
> Some questions are easy and some are more difficult. Do not worry if you find a question hard; just do your best. I hope that you enjoy the test.

At this point, answer any questions that the children ask.

> Now listen carefully to the practice question. You will hear the question twice, then you will have five seconds to work out and write down the answer.
>
> *What is two add seven?*
>
> *What is two add seven?*

Allow the children five seconds to write the answer, then say:

> Put your pencil down.

Check that the children have written the answer to the practice question in the practice question answer box. Remind them that they cannot ask any more questions once the test is started. When you are ready, press start on your CD player.

When the test is finished ask the children to stop writing, then collect the test sheets. For ease of marking we have created a copy of the test paper with the answers entered in the appropriate boxes.

Questions for Test 7

For each of the first five questions you have five seconds to work out and write down the answer.

1   What is four hundred times ten?

2   What is seven squared?

3   What is the difference between thirty-nine and one hundred?

4   Double fifty-three.

5   Write seven tenths as a decimal.

For each of the next questions you have ten seconds to work out and write down the answer.

6   Write the smallest integer you can using the digits eight, one, two, nine, seven.

7   I have a five pound note. I buy a pen for three pounds seventy pence. How much change do I receive?

8   What number is ninety-nine more than one thousand and one?

9   Write three quarters of a litre in millilitres.

10   What number is halfway between eight thousand four hundred and ten thousand.

11   Look at your answer sheet. How much water is in the measuring cylinder?

12   A square has sides of four centimetres. What is its area?

13   How many weeks are there in two years?

14   What number is double one hundred and sixty?

15   Round five thousand one hundred and seventeen to the nearest hundred.

For each of the next five questions you have fifteen seconds to work out and write down the answer.

16   How much money is three quarters of eight pounds?

17   What is the sum of fifteen, twenty-five and eleven?

18   Look at your answer sheet. What number should be written in the box?

19   Write the next number in this sequence: one point six, one point eight, two point zero, two point two.

20   Look at your answer sheet. What is the size of the angle marked A?

Put your pencil down. The test is over.

   Andrew Brodie: Mental Maths Tests 9–10 © A & C Black

Test 7

First name .... Last name ....

School ....

.... **Total marks**

Practice question

Five-second questions

| 1 | | 400 |

| 2 | |

| 3 | | 39 |

| 4 | |

| 5 | | $\frac{7}{10}$ |

Ten-second questions

| 6 | | 8, 1, 2, 9, 7, |

| 7 | £ | £3.70 |

| 8 | | 1001 |

| 9 | ml | $\frac{3}{4}$ l |

| 10 | | 8400 |

| 11 | | ml |

| 12 | | cm² |

| 13 | | weeks |

| 14 | |

| 15 | | 5117 |

Fifteen-second questions

| 16 | £ |

| 17 | | 15, 25, 11 |

| 18 | |

$$60 \div \boxed{} = 2 \times 15$$

| 19 | 1.6, 1.8, 2.0, 2.2,   , … |

| 20 | | ° |

A 45°

Practice question

	9

Five-second questions

1	**4000**	400

2	**49**

3	**61**	39

4	**106**

5	**0.7**	$\frac{7}{10}$

Ten-second questions

6	**12 789**	8, 1, 2, 9, 7,

7	**£1.30**	£3.70

8	**1100**	1001

9	**750** ml	$\frac{3}{4}$ l

10	**9200**	8400

11	**270** ml

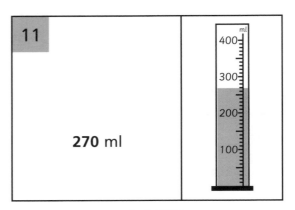

12	**16** cm²

13	**104** weeks

14	**320**

15	**5100**	5117

Fifteen-second questions

16	**£6**

17	**51**	15, 25, 11

18	60 ÷ **2** = 2 x 15

19	1.6, 1.8, 2.0, 2.2, **2.4**, ...

20	**45** °

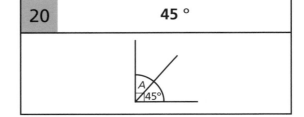

Test 8

Before playing the test on the CD give each child a copy of the test and read out the following script:

Listen to the instructions carefully. I will answer any questions that you have after I have finished reading the instructions to you. Once the test starts you will not be able to ask any questions.

The first question is a practice question. In the test there will then be twenty questions.

Each question has an answer box. Make sure that you only write the answer to the correct question in the box. Try to work out each answer in your head. You can make notes outside the answer box if this helps you but do not try to write out calculations because you will not have enough time. For some questions you will find important information already provided for you.

Each question will be read out twice. Listen carefully then work out your answer. If you cannot do the question, just put a cross. If you make a mistake, do not rub out the wrong answer; cross it out and write the correct answer.

Some questions are easy and some are more difficult. Do not worry if you find a question hard; just do your best. I hope that you enjoy the test.

At this point, answer any questions that the children ask.

Now listen carefully to the practice question. You will hear the question twice, then you will have five seconds to work out and write down the answer.

What is ten take away eight?

What is ten take away eight?

Allow the children five seconds to write the answer, then say:

Put your pencil down.

Check that the children have written the answer to the practice question in the practice question answer box. Remind them that they cannot ask any more questions once the test is started. When you are ready, press start on your CD player.

When the test is finished ask the children to stop writing, then collect the test sheets. For ease of marking we have created a copy of the test paper with the answers entered in the appropriate boxes.

For each of the first five questions you have five seconds to work out and write down the answer.

1   How many ten pence coins are there in two pounds?

2   What is nine squared?

3   What is six hundred divided by ten?

4   Multiply one point seven by ten.

5   Write one hundredth as a decimal.

For each of the next questions you have ten seconds to work out and write down the answer.

6   Four point eight add two point five.

7   What is three times four, add two?

8   What number is ninety-nine less than four hundred and sixty-three?

9   What percentage is equivalent to one tenth?

10   Tom draws a regular pentagon so that it has a perimeter of thirty-five centimetres. What is the length of each side?

11   Write three quarters of a kilometre in metres.

12   Look at your answer sheet. What temperature does the thermometer show?

13   Write the next number in this sequence: sixty-three, fifty-nine, fifty-five, fifty-one.

14   Fifteen percent of the children in a class live in a flat. What percentage do not live in a flat?

15   A rectangle is eight centimetres long and five centimetres wide. What is its area?

For each of the next five questions you have fifteen seconds to work out and write down the answer.

16   I pour six hundred and ninety-one millilitres from a jug containing one litre of water. How much water is left in the jug?

17   Add eighteen to forty-two then subtract twenty-seven.

18   What is the difference between four thousand nine hundred and ninety-nine and nine thousand and seven?

19   Look at your answer sheet. What number should be written in the box?

20   What is twenty-five percent of six hundred?

Put your pencil down. The test is over.

Test 8

First name .... Last name ....

School ....

.... **Total marks** [ ]

Practice question

[ ]

Five-second questions

| 1 | | £2 | [ ] |

| 2 | | [ ] |

| 3 | | 600 | [ ] |

| 4 | | 1.7 | [ ] |

| 5 | | $\frac{1}{100}$ | [ ] |

Ten-second questions

| 6 | | 4.8   2.5 | [ ] |

| 7 | | 3,   4,   2 | [ ] |

| 8 | | 463 | [ ] |

| 9 | % | $\frac{1}{10}$ | [ ] |

| 10 | cm | [ ] |

| 11 | m | $\frac{3}{4}$ km | [ ] |

| 12 | °C | [ ] |

-10   0   10   20   30 °C

| 13 | 63,   59,   55,   51,   ,   … | [ ] |

| 14 | % | 15% | [ ] |

| 15 | cm² | [ ] |

Fifteen-second questions

| 16 | ml | 691 ml | [ ] |

| 17 | | 18, 42, 27 | [ ] |

| 18 | | 4999 9007 | [ ] |

| 19 | | [ ] |

$\frac{3}{4}$ of one hundred = [ ] + 25

| 20 | | [ ] |

Test 8 Answers

Practice question

	2

Five-second questions

1	**20**	£2

2	**81**

3	**60**	600

4	**17**	1.7

5	**0.01**	$\frac{1}{100}$

Ten-second questions

6	**7.3**	4.8 2.5

7	**14**	3, 4, 2

8	**364**	463

9	**10%**	$\frac{1}{10}$

10	**7** cm

11	**750** m	$\frac{3}{4}$ km

12	**-6** °C

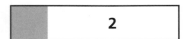

13	63, 59, 55, 51, **47**, …

14	**85%**	15%

15	**40** cm²

Fifteen-second questions

16	**309** ml	691 ml

17	**33**	18, 42, 27

18	**4008**	4999 9007

19	
$\frac{3}{4}$ of one hundred = $\boxed{50}$ + 25	

20	**150**

Test 9

Before playing the test on the CD give each child a copy of the test and read out the following script:

Listen to the instructions carefully. I will answer any questions that you have after I have finished reading the instructions to you. Once the test starts you will not be able to ask any questions.

The first question is a practice question. In the test there will then be twenty questions.

Each question has an answer box. Make sure that you only write the answer to the correct question in the box. Try to work out each answer in your head. You can make notes outside the answer box if this helps you but do not try to write out calculations because you will not have enough time. For some questions you will find important information already provided for you.

Each question will be read out twice. Listen carefully then work out your answer. If you cannot do the question, just put a cross. If you make a mistake, do not rub out the wrong answer; cross it out and write the correct answer.

Some questions are easy and some are more difficult. Do not worry if you find a question hard; just do your best. I hope that you enjoy the test.

At this point, answer any questions that the children ask.

Now listen carefully to the practice question. You will hear the question twice, then you will have five seconds to work out and write down the answer.

What is eleven add three?

What is eleven add three?

Allow the children five seconds to write the answer, then say:

Put your pencil down.

Check that the children have written the answer to the practice question in the practice question answer box. Remind them that they cannot ask any more questions once the test is started. When you are ready, press start on your CD player.

When the test is finished ask the children to stop writing, then collect the test sheets. For ease of marking we have created a copy of the test paper with the answers entered in the appropriate boxes.

Questions for Test 9

For each of the first five questions you have five seconds to work out and write down the answer.

1   What is one tenth of four hundred?

2   What is the square of six?

3   Twenty-three subtract eleven.

4   How much more than fifty-seven is seventy?

5   Double eighty.

For each of the next questions you have ten seconds to work out and write down the answer.

6   Write the biggest integer you can using the digits two, five, six, nine and one.

7   I have a twenty pound note. I buy a DVD for fourteen pounds ninety-nine pence. How much change do I receive?

8   How many hours are there in two days?

9   Write the time two thirty pm as a twenty-four hour clock time.

10 What is ten percent of ninety pounds?

11 Look at your answer sheet. How much water is in the measuring cylinder?

12 One thousand two hundred and thirty-seven subtract five hundred.

13 What is half of four hundred and fifty?

14 A rectangle is seven centimetres long and four centimetres wide. What is its perimeter?

15 Write nine thousand five hundred grams in kilograms.

For each of the next five questions you have fifteen seconds to work out and write down the answer.

16 Four children share some stickers. They have four stickers each and there are two spare stickers. How many stickers are there altogether?

17 Look at your answer sheet. What number should be written in the box?

18 Write the next number in this sequence: five point seven, five point nine, six point one, six point three.

19 What is seventy-five percent of two hundred pounds?

20 I buy a jar of coffee for three pounds forty-seven pence and a box of teabags for two pounds ninety-three pence. How much do I spend altogether?

Put your pencil down. The test is over.

   Andrew Brodie: Mental Maths Tests 9–10 © A & C Black

Test 9

First name .... Last name ....

School ....

....

Total marks

Practice question

Five-second questions

| 1 | | 400 |

| 2 | |

| 3 | |

| 4 | |

| 5 | |

Ten-second questions

| 6 | | 2, 5, 6, 9, 1 |

| 7 | £ | £14.99 |

| 8 | | hours |

| 9 | | 2.30pm |

| 10 | £ |

| 11 | | ml | 400 ml
300
200
100 |

| 12 | | 1237 |

| 13 | | 450 |

| 14 | cm |

| 15 | kg | 9500 g |

Fifteen-second questions

| 16 | |

| 17 | 23 + ☐ = 2 x 16 |

| 18 | 5.7, 5.9, 6.1, 6.3, ____ , ... |

| 19 | £ |

| 20 | £ | £3.47 £2.93 |

Test 9 Answers

Practice question

	14

Five-second questions

1	**40**	400

2	**36**

3	**12**

4	**13**

5	**160**

Ten-second questions

6	**96 521**	2, 5, 6, 9, 1

7	**£5.01**	£14.99

8	**48** hours

9	**14.30**	2.30pm

10	**£9**

11	**310** ml

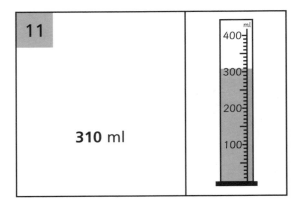

12	**737**	1237

13	**225**	450

14	**22** cm

15	**9.5** kg	9500 g

Fifteen-second questions

16	**18**

17	23 + **9** = 2 × 16

18	5.7, 5.9, 6.1, 6.3, **6.5**, ...

19	**£150**

20	**£6.40**	£3.47 £2.93

  Andrew Brodie: Mental Maths Tests 9–10 © A & C Black

Test 10

Before playing the test on the CD give each child a copy of the test and read out the following script:

Listen to the instructions carefully. I will answer any questions that you have after I have finished reading the instructions to you. Once the test starts you will not be able to ask any questions.

The first question is a practice question. In the test there will then be twenty questions.

Each question has an answer box. Make sure that you only write the answer to the correct question in the box. Try to work out each answer in your head. You can make notes outside the answer box if this helps you but do not try to write out calculations because you will not have enough time. For some questions you will find important information already provided for you.

Each question will be read out twice. Listen carefully then work out your answer. If you cannot do the question, just put a cross. If you make a mistake, do not rub out the wrong answer; cross it out and write the correct answer.

Some questions are easy and some are more difficult. Do not worry if you find a question hard; just do your best. I hope that you enjoy the test.

At this point, answer any questions that the children ask.

Now listen carefully to the practice question. You will hear the question twice, then you will have five seconds to work out and write down the answer.

What is eleven subtract two?

What is eleven subtract two?

Allow the children five seconds to write the answer, then say:

Put your pencil down.

Check that the children have written the answer to the practice question in the practice question answer box. Remind them that they cannot ask any more questions once the test is started. When you are ready, press start on your CD player.

When the test is finished ask the children to stop writing, then collect the test sheets. For ease of marking we have created a copy of the test paper with the answers entered in the appropriate boxes.

Questions for Test 10

For each of the first five questions you have five seconds to work out and write down the answer.

1   What is eight squared?

2   Multiply three point nine by ten.

3   Look at your answer sheet. Draw a ring around the larger number.

4   What must be added to zero point three to make one?

5   What is one third of twelve?

For each of the next questions you have ten seconds to work out and write down the answer.

6   How many groups of three can be made from twenty-two?

7   What is double four point five?

8   Write the smallest integer you can using the digits four, six, five, four and three.

9   How many days are there in four weeks?

10   What number is one hundred and one more than three hundred and ninety-nine?

11   Round one thousand five hundred and thirty-three to the nearest ten.

12   Write eight point five metres in centimetres.

13   A plane journey takes nineteen hours. What fraction of a day is this?

14   Add two hundred and forty-six to five hundred and thirty.

15   What is half of six hundred and fifty?

For each of the next five questions you have fifteen seconds to work out and write down the answer.

16   Look at your answer sheet. What number should be written in the box?

17   Look at your answer sheet. How many rectangles are there in this diagram?

18   A television programme starts at ten forty-five and finishes at eleven twenty-seven. How many minutes long is the programme?

19   The years two thousand and nine and two thousand and ten are not leap years. How many days are there altogether in two thousand and nine and two thousand and ten?

20   There are two hundred and sixty-eight children in a school. One hundred and forty-nine are girls. How many are boys?

Put your pencil down. The test is over.

   Andrew Brodie: Mental Maths Tests 9–10 © A & C Black

Test 10

First name .... Last name ....

School ....

.... **Total marks** [   ]

Practice question

[   ]

Five-second questions

1	

2	3.9

3	28 514	28 415

4	0.3

5	

Ten-second questions

6	22

7	4.5

8	4, 6, 5, 4, 3

9	days

10	399

11	1533

12	cm	8.5m

13	19 hours

14	246

15	650

Fifteen-second questions

16	

$$\square - 8 = 6 \times 7$$

17	rectangles

18	minutes	10.45 pm

19	days	2009, 2010

20	268 149

Test 10 Answers

Practice question

	9

Five-second questions

1	**64**

2	**39**	3.9

3	(**28 514**)	28 415

4	**0.7**	0.3

5	4

Ten-second questions

6	**7**	22

7	**9**	4.5

8	**34 456**	4, 6, 5, 4, 3

9	**28** days

10	**500**	399

11	**1530**	1533

12	**850** cm	8.5 m

13	$\frac{19}{24}$	19 hours

14	**776**	246

15	**325**	650

Fifteen-second questions

16	$\boxed{50} - 8 = 6 \times 7$

17	**9** rectangles

18	**42** minutes	10.45 pm

19	**730** days	2009, 2010

20	**119 boys**	268 149

Pupil record sheet

You may wish to record your pupils' scores as they complete each test .

Page 44 is a record sheet on which you can enter the pupils' names down the left hand column and the dates of the tests along the top. On page 45 there is a graph for recording the scores of each individual pupil. By photocopying this sheet for every member of the class you can monitor each individual's progress from test to test.

It is worth observing where the pupils are making errors. Errors may occur on particular types of question, perhaps where certain vocabulary is used. Is there a pattern to their problems?

You may also find that some pupils find the time restrictions challenging. Do they find the five-second questions more difficult, for example, simply due to the speed with which they have to answer?

Where patterns do emerge you will be able to target your teaching to address the pupils' needs. You should then find improvements as the pupils work through the set of tests.

Pages 46 to 48 provide some extra mental arithmetic practice.

Page 46 features addition squares for practice of number bonds. You may like to set pupils the challenge of completing the squares within a specific time limit.

Page 47 contains two multiplication squares, the first giving practice of all the tables from 2 to 10 and the second covering very useful facts in relation to multiples of 25, 50, 75 and 100. Page 48 gives further practice by presenting the facts in mixed order.

Pupil Record Sheet

Class ....

Test number:	1	2	3	4	5	6	7	8	9	10
Date:										
Name:										

Pupil Progress Graph

Name...

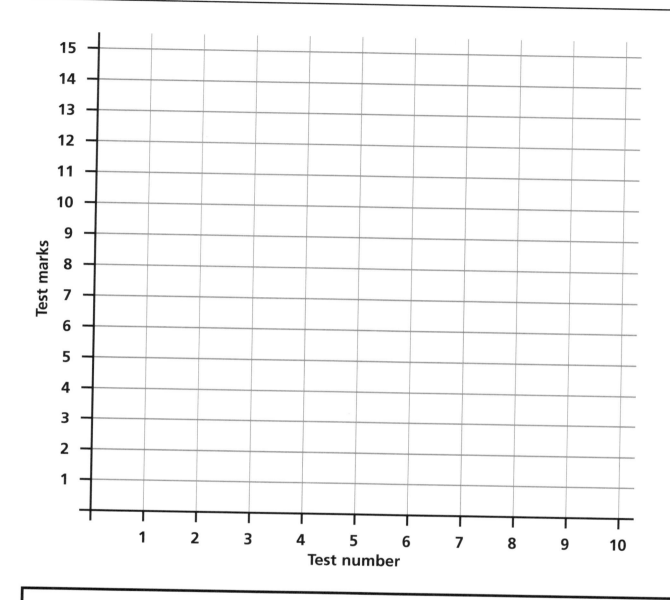

Comments, including any particular areas of difficulty

Addition squares

Name..

+	1	2	3	4	5	6	7	8	9	10
1										
2										
3										
4										
5										
6										
7										
8										
9										
10										

+	25	50	75	100
25				
50				
75				
100				

 Andrew Brodie: Mental Maths Tests 9–10 © A & C Black

Multiplication squares

Name..

x	2	3	4	5	6	7	8	9	10
2									
3									
4									
5									
6									
7									
8									
9									
10									

x	25	50	75	100
1				
2				
3				
4				

Mixed multiplication squares

Name...

x	2	7	3	9	4	6	8	5	10
6									
5									
9									
3									
7									
2									
8									
4									
10									

x	50	100	75	200	25
4					
2					
3					
1					
5					